THE OPEN MINDED TAROT WORKBOOK

Kate Ross

Vodnik Publishing

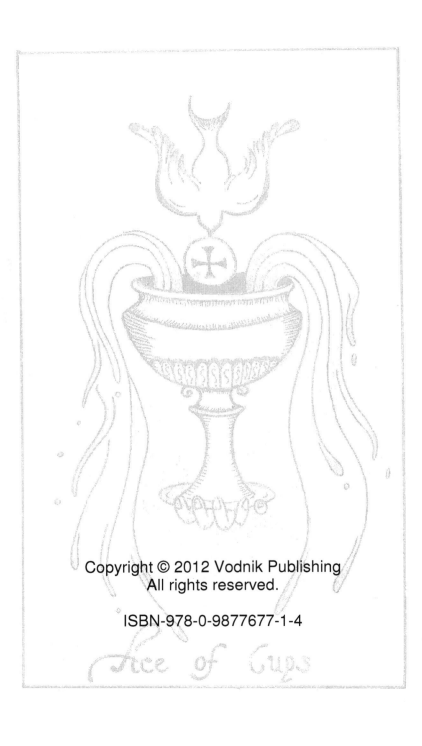

ISBN-978-0-9877677-1-4

Table of Contents

4

Welcome to the Open Minded Tarot Workbook. I originally designed these exercises for a student who was interested in learning the tarot and have since expanded them. The exercises presented in this book will help you to deepen your readings and more fully interpret the cards you find in your spreads.

It can be used in conjunction with The Open Minded Tarot: a Practical Guide, but that is not required. The exercises have been designed to be as flexible as possible so as to accommodate people who have learned in every possible tradition. The meanings of the cards may differ from reader to reader, but the human condition is always the same. We all experience love, fear, sadness, anger, victory and defeat. It is by learning to connect these emotions and events with specific cards that we can create a fuller and more mature reading for the Querent.

One thing I have included is the idea of reading combinations. I feel that cards cannot be read standing alone. Instead, the cards need to be read in pairs and groups in order to get a better picture of what is going on in the life of a Querent. Reading tarot is like telling a story, and a story can rarely be told in one sentence alone. Included are exercises in pairs, but once you have mastered reading two cards in tandem, it will be no great thing to read three or four together.

Reading tarot is a wonderful way of deepening your understanding of the world around you. I wish you a great journey.

Kate Ross

GETTING COMFORTABLE WITH THE CARDS

It's impossible to learn to read tarot overnight. It's a long process and it requires dedication and observation. Reading for other people is a great responsibility so it's vital that you've studied diligently. It isn't enough to read one book and consider yourself ready.

I strongly recommend that in order to enrich your understanding of the cards, you read as many sources as possible. There are many different interpretations and it would be foolish to say that only one way is the correct way. I began learning about tarot twenty years ago and in all that time I've been open to reading and learning as much as I could. My interpretations of cards today are quite different than they were when I started out and you will likely find this to be the case as well. You may find that you disagree with the interpretations I have provided here and that's perfectly fine. Find your own way.

You will notice the terms "Dignified" and "Ill-Dignified" used in this workbook. A dignified card is a card which is turned 'the right way' when you lay in on the table, an ill-dignified card is a card which is upside-down, or reversed. You will see the term "ID" which is the abbreviation I use for an ill-dignified card. If not specified, the card is not reversed.

The best way to get comfortable reading and interpreting the cards is to use them every day. Use a notebook as a tarot journal and write down your ideas and impressions of the cards you see. Make some time each morning (two or three minutes is enough) to quickly shuffle the deck and pull one card. Look at the card and in your journal write down the name of the card and a few of the qualities it contains. Then, throughout the day, think about that card. Consider the following:

> *Is the card right side up (Dignified) or reversed (also called 'Ill Dignified' or "ID")?*
> *What does this card mean?*
> *Why did it come up, today of all days?*
> *Does it apply to your life in some way?*
> *Does it apply to someone you know?*
> *If the card represents a person, who is that person?*
> *What lessons does it contain?*
> *What does it teach us?*

At the end of the day, jot down a few observations and notes.

After you have been doing this for several months and are starting to feel comfortable, start pulling two cards at a time and look at them, not as individual cards, but as cards which compliment each other. Ask yourself the following:

> *Do these cards have anything in common?*
> *What is the main message of each of them?*
> *Is there a place where these messages intersect?*
> *Do they tell a story?*
> *Do they apply to your life or the life of someone you know?*
> *Does it look like cause and effect?*
> *Does it look like one card modifies the other?*

Write the combination down in your tarot journal. You will be surprised to see how your interpretations stretch and change as time goes on.

READING "BACKWARDS"

One valuable way of learning how to interpret cards is by reading "backwards". That is to say that instead of looking at a card and saying how it applies to the Querent's life, it is also possible to think of a person or situation and say which card can be used to describe them.

For example, imagine that you have an elderly aunt who is stuck in the past. She speaks constantly of people she knew and events which took place decades ago. Her nostalgia for the past keeps her from enjoying the present or looking forward to the future. You could say, in this case, that the Six of Cups (ID) could be used to describe her, as it is a card that speaks of nostalgia which has gone too far, of living in the past to the detriment of the present.

If one of your co-workers is a person who delights in spreading rumours and indulging in malicious gossip, you could connect his behaviour to the Page of Swords. The Page of Swords (ID) can be interpreted as rumour, gossip and innuendo.

Naturally, people are not one-dimensional and there is more than one way to describe any given person. Someone may be unorganised and prone to chaos in their lives, but they may also be generous, kind and a genuinely good friend. Another person may be honest and hard working but struggle with an addiction of some sort that wreaks havoc in their life.

Which cards would you use to describe yourself?

My good qualities are represented by:

_____

_____

My negative qualities are represented by:

_____

_____

Using the technique of reading backwards, think about five events from your past which were important to you. They could be either of a positive or negative nature. Which cards could be used to describe:

1. Event: _____

   The onset of the event:_____

   The event itself: _____

   The aftermath of the event: _____

2. Event: _____

   The onset of the event:_____

   The event itself: _____

   The aftermath of the event: _____

3. Event: _____

   The onset of the event:_____

   The event itself: _____

   The aftermath of the event: _____

4. Event: _____

   The onset of the event: _____

   The event itself: _____

   The aftermath of the event: _____

5. Event: _____

   The onset of the event: _____

   The event itself: _____

   The aftermath of the event: _____

Think about five events in the life of a close friend or family member. These events could be of a positive or negative nature. Which cards can be used to describe these events? You can choose different people if you like.

1. Who: _____

   Event: _____

   The onset of the event: _____

   The event itself: _____

   The aftermath of the event: _____

2. Who: _____

   Event: _____

   The onset of the event:_____

   The event itself: _____

   The aftermath of the event: _____

3. Who: _____

   Event:_____

   The onset of the event:_____

   The event itself: _____

   The aftermath of the event: _____

4. Who: _____

   Event:_____

   The onset of the event:_____

   The event itself: _____

   The aftermath of the event: _____

5. Who: _____

   Event: _____

   The onset of the event: _____

   The event itself: _____

   The aftermath of the event: _____

Take a look at this list of people and decide which cards you associate with them or their lives. People are multi-faceted so lay more than one card if you think it applies. There is no right or wrong answer. Trust your intuition.

Tony Blair _____

Marilyn Monroe _____

Jacqueline Onassis _____

Ernest Hemingway _____

Vincent Van Gogh _____

Oprah Winfrey _____

The Prime Minister /
President of your country _____

John Belushi _____

13

William Shakespeare _____

Elvis Presley _____

Michael Jordan _____

Mahatma Ghandi _____

Abraham Lincoln _____

Elizabeth Taylor _____

James Dean _____

Clint Eastwood _____

Martin Luther King _____

Isaac Newton _____

Christopher Columbus _____

Albert Einstein _____

John Lennon _____

Harry Houdini _____

Billie Holiday _____

Mother Teresa _____

Oscar Wilde _____

Stalin _____

Queen Victoria _____

Genghis Kahn _____

Now do the same exercise using people from your own life. Decide which card/combination of cards best describes your:

Favourite singer _____

Least favourite singer _____

Favourite song _____

Favourite actor _____

Least favourite actor _____

Favourite film _____

Favourite teacher _____

Least favourite teacher _____

Brother _____

Sister _____

Cousin _____

Boss _____

Partner _____

Neighbour _____

Best friend _____

Mother _____

Father _____

Grandmother _____

Grandfather _____

Aunt _____

Uncle _____

Co-worker _____

Former partner(s) _____

Best friend from high school _____

The school bully _____

Now think about these emotions / qualities / actions and decide which cards they remind you of. There is no right or wrong answer. Trust your instincts.

Love is an emotion which we all feel and which takes many forms and inspires many different actions. Some of these are positive, others less so. Which cards do you feel correspond to the following?

Love _____

Longing _____

Desire _____

Kindness _____

Generosity _____

Lust _____

Jealousy _____

Affection _____

Adoration _____

Fondness _____

Liking someone _____

Attraction _____

Caring _____

Tenderness _____

Compassion _____

Sentimentality _____

Arousal _____

Passion _____

Infatuation _____

Obsession _____

Having a crush _____

Betrayal _____

Yearning _____

Sadness is an emotion which we all feel, whether we admit it or not. Sadness takes many forms and is something most people try to avoid by distracting themselves with anything they can think of. Which cards do you feel correspond to the following?

Sadness _____

Feeling tortured _____

Being rejected _____

Feeling lost _____

Agony _____

Suffering _____

Hurt _____

Anguish _____

Depression _____

Despair _____

Hopelessness _____

Gloom _____

Nostalgia _____

Grief _____

Homesickness _____

Sorrow _____

Misery _____

Melancholy _____

Disappointment _____

Dismay _____

Ace of Cups

Anger is generally thought of as being a negative emotion but this is not always the case. Many great changes in society and indeed, in our own lives were brought on by anger. Anger is often perfectly justified; it's how we express it and what we do with it that needs to be carefully cultivated. Which cards do you feel correspond to the following?

Anger _____

Irritation _____

Aggravation _____

Agitation _____

Annoyance _____

Grouchiness _____

Exasperation _____

Frustration _____

Rage _____

Outrage _____

Fury _____

Wrath _____

Hostility _____

Ferocity _____

Bitterness _____

Hate _____

Scorn _____

Spite _____

Vengefulness _____

Dislike _____

Resentment _____

Disgust _____

Revulsion _____

Contempt _____

Loathing _____

Envy _____

Revenge _____

Nastiness _____

Stabbing someone in the back _____

22

Fear is one of the elemental emotions. We fear what we do not know and this fear of the unknown can lead to disgust and disdain. Facing your fears can make you stronger and more tolerant of the world around you. Which cards do you feel correspond to the following emotions?

Fear _____

Alarm _____

Shock _____

Fright _____

Horror _____

Terror _____

Panic _____

Hysteria _____

Nervousness _____

Anxiety _____

Tenseness _____

Uneasiness _____

Apprehension _____

Worry _____

Distress _____

Dread _____

Suspicion _____

Timidity _____

Shyness _____

Finding courage _____

Ace of Cups

Happiness is what we all aspire to. There are many forms of happiness from joy, which is fleeting, to serenity and contentment. Which cards do you feel correspond to the following?

Happiness _____

Cheerfulness _____

Amusement _____

Bliss _____

Joviality _____

Joy _____

Delight _____

Enjoyment _____

Gladness _____

Elation _____

Satisfaction _____

Euphoria _____

Zest _____

Enthusiasm _____

Excitement _____

Exhilaration _____

Pleasure _____

Pride _____

Triumph _____

Optimism _____

Eagerness _____

Hope _____

Enthrallment _____

Surprise _____

Amazement _____

Keenness _____

Earnest _____

Contentment _____

Serenity _____

Shame is something we learn from the society around us. We can feel shame when we have behaved badly and we are sorry about what we've done or we can feel shame when others tell us we are not good enough. Which cards do you feel correspond to the following emotions?

Shame _____

Guilt _____

Regret _____

Remorse _____

Alienation _____

Isolation _____

Loneliness _____

Rejection _____

Defeat _____

Dejection _____

Insecurity _____

Embarrassment _____

Humiliation _____

Insulted _____

Pity _____

Which cards correspond to the following?

Foolishness _____

Truth _____

Untruth _____

Stupidity _____

Refusing to see reality _____

Cheating on a partner _____

Stealing _____

Gossip _____

Leadership _____

Decency _____

Relief _____

Abandoning a sinking ship _____

Decision making _____

Creativity _____

Hard work _____

Modesty _____

Arrogance _____

Industriousness _____

Loyalty through problems _____

Thrift _____

Greed _____

Realistic vision of the future _____

Distorted vision of the future _____

Realistic vision of the past _____

Distorted vision of the past _____

Religious tendencies _____

Rigid thinking _____

Flexibility _____

Riches _____

Poverty _____

Pride at the cost of comfort _____

Feeling burdened _____

Karma _____

Balance _____

Depravity _____

Addiction _____

Fundamentalist religious ideas _____

Apathy _____

Inaction _____

Being sorry for your actions _____

Being unrepentant for your actions _____

Cheating to win _____

Being a sore loser _____

Crime _____

Punishment _____

Reward _____

Neglect _____

Studying for a profession_____

Discovering the disappointing
truth about someone you love _____

Hard work _____

Gluttony _____

Sexual problems _____

Theft _____

Marriage _____

Divorce _____

Getting a new job _____

Losing a job _____

Making friends _____

Finding love _____

The following exercises are based on interpretations of the cards given in The Open Minded Tarot: A Practical Guide. They may or may not also correspond to other books you have read or to your own personal belief of what a card means. This is in no way problematic as you can still use these exercises to enhance your study of the tarot. Simply take the situation given and write down which card you feel it corresponds to. There are answers given at the back (page 186), but feel free to disregard them if they do not correspond to your own learning of tarot.

These exercises are divided not into suits but by numbers. Therefore, all the Aces are in one section and the Twos, Threes, Fours etc all have their own exercises. Each "Situations" section has eight examples, two for each suit, (Cups, Wands, Swords and Coins) one Dignified and one Ill-Dignified.

Ill-Dignified (also known as "Reversed) refers to a card that is laid on the table upside down, so that the top of the card is turned 180 degrees. For the purposes of brevity, I have simply abbreviated it to ID. For example, Two of Cups ID indicates the Two of Cups Reversed. Where there is no ID specified, the card is "right –side up".

MINOR ARCANA EXERCISES

ACES: SITUATIONS

Which of these situations remind you of the various Aces? Are they Dignified or Ill Dignified?

a) The Querent has decided to go back to school to get her Master's degree in Education.

_____

b) The Querent has started a love affair with a married man.

_____

c) The Querent is determined to take control of his finances and start saving and investing.

_____

d) The Querent has decided to end a friendship that has been one-sided and difficult.

_____

e) The Querent's husband has been acting in a negatively aggressive way, pushing away the people who care about him.

_____

f) The Querent has been feeling listless and apathetic.

_____

g) The Querent is consumed with worries about money.

_____

h) The Querent enjoys a loving relationship with her partner and hopes to start a family.

_____

Look at these combinations and write down what they make you think of. There is no right or wrong answer, use your intuition. Remember that "ID" stands for Ill Dignified (Reversed)

Ace of Swords, the Devil ID

_____

_____

Ace of Swords, Six of Wands

_____

_____

Ace of Swords ID, the Lovers

_____

_____

Ace of Swords ID, the Tower

_____

_____

Ace of Cups, the Empress

_____

_____

Ace of Cups, Two of Swords

_____

_____

Ace of Cups ID, the Star

_____

_____

Ace of Cups ID, Six of Cups ID

_____

_____

Ace of Wands ID, the Tower

_____

_____

Ace of Wands ID, Four of Swords ID

_____

_____

Ace of Wands, Eight of Coins

_____

_____

Ace of Wands, Nine of Coins

_____

_____

Ace of Coins ID, the Tower ID

_____

_____

Ace of Coins ID, Five of Coins

_____

_____

Ace of Coins, the Emperor

_____

_____

Ace of Coins, Nine of Coins

_____

_____

Which of these situations remind you of the various Twos? Are they Dignified or Ill Dignified?

a) The Querent is thinking about taking a better paying job, but it would mean that she must make an expensive move far away from family and friends.

_____

b) The Querent has met a fantastic person and is enjoying a loving and balanced relationship.

_____

c) The Querent works constantly and is beginning to feel run down and negative.

_____

d) The Querent's husband has been out of work for a while. He sits at home and does very little. He's been offered work but he doesn't seem interested in anything.

_____

e) The Querent is preparing to go back to school to learn a trade. He's very excited about the prospect of changing his life.

_____

f) The Querent suspects her business partner is cheating her somehow.

_____

g) The Querent is in a long-term relationship that isn't working. She's thinking of leaving.

_____

h) The Querent is in a long-term relationship that isn't working. He doesn't have the confidence to break-up with his partner.

_____

Look at these combinations and write down what they make you think of. There is no right or wrong answer, use your intuition. Remember that "ID" stands for Ill Dignified (Reversed)

Two of Wands, the Devil

_____

_____

Two of Wands, the Chariot

_____

_____

Two of Wands ID, Seven of Swords ID

_____

_____

Two of Wands ID, the Tower

_____

_____

41

Two of Swords, Ten of Swords

_____

_____

Two of Swords, the Lovers

_____

_____

Two of Swords ID, Four of Cups ID

_____

_____

Two of Swords ID, Seven of Coins ID

_____

_____

Two of Cups ID, the Empress ID

_____

_____

Two of Cups ID, Page of Swords

_____

_____

Two of Cups, Six of Cups

_____

_____

Two of Cups, Four of Wands

_____

_____

Two of Coins, the Lovers ID

_____

_____

Two of Coins, Three of Coins ID

_____

_____

Two of Coins ID, Justice

_____

_____

Two of Coins ID, Temperance ID

_____

_____

Which of these situations remind you of the various Threes? Are they Dignified or Ill Dignified?

a) The Querent works in a humble job in which she takes great pride. She is careful and diligent and she enjoys what she does.

_____

b) The Querent and her husband are trying to have a baby.

_____

c) The Querent has been having relationship troubles with his girlfriend and it's only getting worse.

_____

d) The Querent is incredibly depressed over the loss of her mother. She is overcome with grief.

_____

e) The Querent has a new business plan and is busy getting organised. He is energetic and positive and it looks as though his business will be a great success.

_____

f) The Querent's new co-worker is a bully and a braggart. He claims he is better than anyone else and yet when asked to perform a task, he makes himself scarce.

_____

g) The Querent's life is flat and unhappy. She goes to clubs and goes home with men she neither likes nor cares for. She feels ashamed but continues.

_____

h) The Querent is working on a project at university with three other people. The group has fallen into disarray and the Querent is concerned as a large part of her mark is going to be based on this project. The others seem lazy and unconcerned.

_____

Look at these combinations and write down what they make you think of. There is no right or wrong answer, use your intuition. Remember that "ID" stands for Ill Dignified (Reversed)

Three of Coins, Two of Wands

_____

_____

Three of Coins, Ace of Swords

_____

_____

Three of Coins ID, the Fool ID

_____

_____

Three of Coins ID, Four of Swords

_____

_____

Three of Swords, the Empress ID

_____

_____

Three of Swords, the Moon

_____

_____

Three of Swords ID, the Star ID

_____

_____

Three of Swords ID, Seven of Swords

_____

_____

Three of Wands, Two of Coins

_____

_____

Three of Wands, Eight of Coins

_____

_____

Three of Wands ID, the Fool

_____

_____

Three of Wands ID, Seven of Coins ID

_____

_____

Three of Cups, Strength

_____

_____

Three of Cups, the Devil

_____

_____

Three of Cups ID, Justice ID

_____

_____

Three of Cups ID, Temperance

_____

_____

FOURS: SITUATIONS

Which of these situations remind you of the various fours? Are they Dignified or Ill Dignified?

a) The Querent is planning a holiday to Mexico

---

b) The Querent went through a rough time five years ago and still can't get himself together.

---

c) The Querent's father-in-law is a miser whose cheapness is making her miserable.

---

d) The Querent has a nice life but she's bored. She's restless and wants something new.

---

e) The Querent does not appreciate all the good things in her life and is behaving like a spoiled child.

---

f) The Querent has been through a rough time and needs a break.

---

g) The Querent had been acting like a partying teenager for years. She's thirty-seven now, and her immaturity has cost her friends and relationships.

_____

h) The Querent is spending money a bit too freely and needs to be more careful. It's not terribly serious, but it's better to adopt more prudent habits.

_____

FOURS: COMBINATIONS

Look at these combinations and write down what they make you think of. There is no right or wrong answer, use your intuition. Remember that "ID" stands for Ill Dignified (Reversed)

Four of Swords ID, the Moon

_____

_____

Four of Swords ID, Four of Cups

_____

_____

Four of Swords, Three of Wands

_____

_____

Four of Swords, Seven of Coins

_____

_____

Four of Cups, Two of Cups

_____

_____

Four of Cups, the Emperor ID

_____

_____

Four of Cups ID, the Empress ID

_____

_____

Four of Cups ID, the High Priestess ID

_____

_____

Four of Wands, the Magician

_____

_____

Four of Wands, Page of Cups

_____

_____

Four of Wands ID, Ace of Wands ID

_____

_____

Four of Wands ID, the Tower

_____

_____

Four of Coins, the Emperor ID

_____

_____

Four of Coins, the Devil

_____

_____

Four of Coins ID, Nine of Cups ID

_____

_____

Four of Coins ID, Five of Coins

_____

_____

Which of these situations remind you of the various fives? Are they Dignified or Ill Dignified?

a) The Querent is trapped in an abusive relationship. He sees no way out and it is causing him incredible pain.

_____

b) The Querent is up for a promotion at work and is too shy to tell her boss how badly she wants this.

_____

c) The Querent was left by her husband three years ago and can't seem to let go of her pain and sadness.

_____

d) The Querent was rude to someone at work. He feels sorry about it and thinks he should apologise.

_____

e) The Querent is having money problems but doesn't want to admit it. She is going to lose her house. She could ask her parents for help but she's ashamed.

_____

f) The Querent is very envious of her sister. It's affecting her relationship with her family. She believes her sister "gets everything" and she is left with nothing.

---

g) The Querent and his girlfriend broke up recently and he is trying to put the pieces of his life back together. He is trying to look on the bright side and focus on the good that he has in his life.

---

h) The Querent is apathetic and doesn't care about her job. Her co-workers avoid asking her for assistance and her boss has started delegating her work to others. She fears her boss could be preparing to fire her.

FIVES: COMBINATIONS

Look at these combinations and write down what they make you think of. There is no right or wrong answer, use your intuition. Remember that "ID" stands for Ill Dignified (Reversed)

Five of Swords, Three of Coins ID

_____

_____

Five of Swords, Page of Swords ID

_____

_____

Five of Swords ID, Emperor ID

_____

_____

Five of Swords ID, Four of Wands ID

_____

_____

Five of Coins, Four of Cups

_____

_____

Five of Coins, Ten of Cups ID

_____

_____

Five of Coins ID, Justice ID

_____

_____

Five of Coins ID, Six of Wands ID

_____

_____

Five of Cups, Three of Swords

_____

_____

Five of Cups, Ace of Swords

_____

_____

Five of Cups ID, Three of Wands ID

_____

_____

Five of Cups ID, the Moon

_____

_____

Five of Wands, Three of Wands

_____

_____

Five of Wands, Ace of Cups

_____

_____

Five of Wands ID, Six of Wands ID

_____

_____

Five of Wands ID, Justice

_____

_____

Which of these situations remind you of the various Sixes? Are they Dignified or Ill Dignified?

a) The Querent is longing for a lover who left him years ago. He is unable to function in his daily life and his nostalgia has turned into obsession.

_____

b) The Querent's boss doesn't believe the economic downturn will affect his department. He refuses to consider the possibility that they will lose money and so he's not open to trying anything new to attract business.

_____

c) The Querent's sister is in financial trouble. She's thinking of helping her out by asking her to come and live with her.

_____

d) The Querent is considering asking his mother for money, even though she is a difficult woman.

_____

e) The Querent has just gone through a divorce. She's slowly getting back on her feet.

_____

f) The Querent has recently managed to convince a client to invest a great deal of money in her company. She is the hero of the hour in her workplace.

_____

g) The Querent receives an unexpected visit from an old friend. It's a welcome visit, one he thoroughly enjoys.

_____

h) The Querent has just learned that her husband is leaving her for another woman.

_____

Look at these combinations and write down what they make you think of. There is no right or wrong answer, use your intuition. Remember that "ID" stands for Ill Dignified (Reversed)

Six of Cups, the Lovers

_____

_____

Six of Cups, Two of Cups

_____

_____

Six of Cups ID, Knight of Swords

_____

_____

Six of Cups ID, Knight of Cups ID

_____

_____

Six of Swords, Queen of Swords ID

_____

_____

Six of Swords, the Fool

_____

_____

Six of Swords ID, the Devil

_____

_____

Six of Swords ID, the World ID

_____

_____

Six of Wands, Five of Swords

_____

_____

Six of Wands, Ace of Wands

_____

_____

Six of Wands ID, Three of Cups ID

_____

_____

Six of Wands ID, the Empress

_____

_____

Six of Coins, Three of Coins

_____

_____

Six of Coins, High Priestess ID

_____

_____

Six of Coins ID, the Tower

_____

_____

Six of Coins ID, Judgement ID

_____

_____

Which of these situations remind you of the various Sevens? Are they Dignified or Ill Dignified?

a) The Querent had hoped for a promotion but her lack of preparation caused her boss to give it to a rival. She's disappointed.

_____

b) The Querent feels he has to choose between two women and he's not sure what to do. Neither of them would be his "perfect" partner and yet he feels compelled to make a decision.

_____

c) The Querent is completely exhausted from work and family responsibilities. She literally cannot take anymore.

_____

d) The Querent invested some money only to find he had been conned. The loss is not devastating but he is angry and embarrassed.

_____

e) The Querent dreams of becoming a famous singer but she hasn't got much of a voice. She imagines she's going to be rich and famous and adored.

_____

f) The Querent was humiliated at work by one of her colleagues who directed rude remarks towards her. One by one, her co-workers are approaching her to tell her how horrified they were, and how they felt powerless to stop him.

_____

g) The Querent is under attack from all sides. Her husband is angry because she works too much, her boss is angry because she doesn't work enough, her kids feel neglected, her co-workers feel put upon.

_____

Look at these combinations and write down what they make you think of. There is no right or wrong answer, use your intuition. Remember that "ID" stands for Ill Dignified (Reversed)

Seven of Cups, Four of Cups

_____

_____

Seven of Cups, Five of Swords

_____

_____

Seven of Cups ID, Two of Wands ID

_____

_____

Seven of Cups ID, the Star

_____

_____

71

Seven of Swords, Temperance

_____

_____

Seven of Swords, Five of Swords

_____

_____

Seven of Swords ID, Justice ID

_____

_____

Seven of Swords ID, the Emperor

_____

_____

Seven of Wands, the Tower

_____

_____

Seven of Wands, Ace of Cups

_____

_____

Seven of Wands ID, Knight of Wands ID

_____

_____

Seven of Wands ID, Five of Wands

_____

_____

Seven of Coins, the Fool

_____

_____

Seven of Coins, Death

_____

_____

Seven of Coins ID, the Chariot ID

_____

_____

Seven of Coins ID, Three of Swords

_____

_____

Which of these situations remind you of the various Eights? Are they Dignified or Ill Dignified?

a) The Querent overhears a telephone conversation which calls into question the honesty of her partner. She has long suspected there is a problem.

_____

b) The Querent's brother has moved in with her. He's been fired from his job and spends the day laying about and watching television.

_____

c) The Querent lost an important client due to a lack of care. She's embarrassed and is determined to do better.

_____

d) The Querent is stuck in an unhappy relationship. She continues to try to "make it work" but to no avail.

_____

e) The Querent found out only after signing a contract that her new business partner is a person of questionable morals. She's worried about the future consequences of working with this person.

_____

f) The Querent has left a relationship which offered her very little. She's moved to a new town and started a new job.

_____

g) The Querent's life is a disaster. She refuses to take responsibility for anything that has gone wrong and continues to blame others for her current situation.

_____

h) The Querent is in an unhappy relationship which she feels she cannot leave. It is beginning to wear her down and she's becoming physically ill due to the stress in her life.

_____

Look at these combinations and write down what they make you think of. There is no right or wrong answer, use your intuition. Remember that "ID" stands for Ill Dignified (Reversed)

Eight of Cups, Five of Cups

_____

_____

Eight of Cups, the Empress ID

_____

_____

Eight of Cups ID, Six of Cups ID

_____

_____

Eight of Cups ID, the Lovers ID

_____

_____

Eight of Swords, Two Cups ID

_____

_____

Eight of Swords, Five of Swords

_____

_____

Eight of Swords ID, Six of Swords

_____

_____

Eight of Swords ID, Queen of Coins ID

_____

_____

Eight of Wands, Ace of Cups

_____

_____

Eight of Wands, Ace of Swords

_____

_____

Eight of Wands ID, the Tower

_____

_____

Eight of Wands ID, Page of Swords ID

_____

_____

Eight of Coins, Three of Coins

_____

_____

Eight of Coins, Four of Wands

_____

_____

Eight of Coins ID, the World ID

_____

_____

Eight of Coins ID, Temperance ID

_____

_____

Which of these situations remind you of the various Nines? Are they Dignified or Ill Dignified?

a) The Querent has reached a level of success in his life and is feeling somewhat smug about his position.

_____

b) The Querent's spending is out of control and she risks losing her home if she continues in this manner.

_____

c) The Querent has a tendency to blow up small problems to huge proportions causing him undue stress and anxiety.

_____

d) The Querent is having a difficult time with her mother-in-law. They have been sniping at each other for years. The Querent wonders if it isn't time for her to just stop participating in this petty fight.

_____

e) After working for many years of frugal and careful living, the Querent and his wife have retired in luxury.

_____

f) The Querent's mother is deeply depressed and is perhaps suicidal as well.

_____

g) The Querent has a great deal of money and refuses to help her daughter who's going through a difficult divorce. She believes that divorce is shameful and is embarrassed by her daughter.

_____

h) The Querent's boss has lately become very aggressive and ill-mannered. He shouts at employees and has been rude to clients. The Querent is concerned he's going to drive away business if he continues like this.

_____

NINES: COMBINATIONS

Look at these combinations and write down what they make you think of. There is no right or wrong answer, use your intuition. Remember that "ID" stands for Ill Dignified (Reversed)

Nine of Cups, Two of Cups ID

_____

_____

Nine of Cups, Four of Coins

_____

_____

Nine of Cups ID, Five of Coins

_____

_____

Nine of Cups ID, the High Priestess

_____

_____

Nine of Swords, the Moon

_____

_____

Nine of Swords, Three of Wands ID

_____

_____

Nine of Swords ID, Six of Cups ID

_____

_____

Nine of Swords ID, Queen of Wands ID

_____

_____

Nine of Wands, Eight of Wands

_____

_____

Nine of Wands, Eight of Coins

_____

_____

Nine of Wands ID, Ace of Swords ID

_____

_____

Nine of Wands ID, Knight of Cups ID

_____

_____

Nine of Coins, Five of Coins

_____

_____

Nine of Coins, Ace of Coins

_____

_____

Nine of Coins ID, Ten of Swords ID

_____

_____

Nine of Coins ID, Two of Wands ID

_____

_____

TENS: SITUATIONS

Which of these situations remind you of the various Tens? Are they Dignified or Ill Dignified?

a) The Querent and her husband have a lovely family life. They are not rich but they have enough, live happily and have children who enrich their lives.

_____

b) The Querent's husband refuses to accept that his daughter wants to marry a man from a different culture. Their daughter is threatening never to speak to them again. The Querent is caught in the middle.

_____

c) The Querent's relationship with her mother is very damaging. Her mother is always playing the victim and frequently threatens suicide if she doesn't get her way. Recently she took too many pills and had to be taken to the hospital. The Querent fears her mother may take her own life.

_____

d) The Querent is a busy man with a business to run, and a family with four small children. He and his wife are well organised and manage to make time for everything.

_____

e) The Querent's home life is very difficult. Her mother-in-law lives with them and she is very aggressive with her old-fashioned ideas. It is causing a rift between the Querent and her husband

_____

f) The Querent has recently been given a huge amount of responsibility at work and now finds herself paralyzed with fear. She is afraid to admit she doesn't know what she's doing. The situation is getting out of hand.

_____

g) The Querent and her husband have no children and are about to retire. They have plenty of money saved up and are going to travel. They live graciously.

_____

h) The Querent betrayed her best friend by sleeping with her husband. She knows what she's done is wrong, but she plans to continue the affair.

_____

TENS: COMBINATIONS

Look at these combinations and write down what they make you think of. There is no right or wrong answer, use your intuition. Remember that "ID" stands for Ill Dignified (Reversed)

Ten of Cups, Two of Cups

_____

_____

Ten of Cups, Five of Coins

_____

_____

Ten of Cups ID, Seven of Coins

_____

_____

Ten of Cups ID, Two of Swords

_____

_____

Ten of Swords, Five of Swords ID

_____

_____

Ten of Swords, the Devil

_____

_____

Ten of Swords ID, Page of Swords ID

_____

_____

Ten of Swords ID, Queen of Swords

_____

_____

Ten of Wands, Five of Swords ID

_____

_____

Ten of Wands, the Tower

_____

_____

Ten of Wands ID, Five of Cups

_____

_____

Ten of Wands ID, Eight of Wands ID

_____

_____

Ten of Coins, Ace of Wands

_____

_____

Ten of Coins, Eight of Coins,

_____

_____

Ten of Coins ID, Justice

_____

_____

Ten of Coins ID, King of Wands ID

_____

_____

Which of these situations remind you of the various Pages? Are they Dignified or Ill Dignified?

a) The Querent's younger sister is very difficult. She's moody, she invents things in order to gain sympathy and she is very selfish.

_____

b) The Querent's younger brother is focused on money to the exclusion of all else. He can be quite rude and has very strict ideas about how one should live. The Querent finds him exasperating and boring.

_____

c) The Querent's co-worker is a vicious rumour-monger. This person is creating havoc in the work place.

_____

d) The Querent is expecting a baby.

_____

e) The Querent has just discovered that someone she took for a friend has betrayed her by telling other people things the Querent had said in confidence.

_____

f) The Querent is a young man. He's very serious and though he means well and has good intentions, his social skills are poor and he has a difficult time making friends.

_____

g) The Querent is full of energy and optimism. She has many friends and is generally considered a loyal and positive person.

_____

h) The Querent is very honest and enjoys observing others. He's incredibly good at sniffing out a lie.

_____

Look at these combinations and write down what they make you think of. There is no right or wrong answer, use your intuition. Remember that "ID" stands for Ill Dignified (Reversed)

Page of Cups, Ace of Wands

_____

_____

Page of Cups, the Emperor

_____

_____

Page of Cups ID, Nine of Swords

_____

_____

Page of Cups ID, Eight of Cups

_____

_____

95

Page of Swords, Four of Cups

_____

_____

Page of Swords, the Fool ID

_____

_____

Page of Swords ID, Justice

_____

_____

Page of Swords ID, Justice

_____

_____

Page of Wands, Two of Wands ID

_____

_____

Page of Wands, Three of Coins

_____

_____

Page of Wands ID, the Magician ID

_____

_____

Page of Wands ID, Ace of Swords ID

_____

_____

Page of Coins, Six of Coins ID

_____

_____

Page of Coins, Seven of Cups

_____

_____

Page of Coins ID, Two of Swords

_____

_____

Page of Coins ID, Four of Coins ID

_____

_____

Which of these situations remind you of the various Knights? Are they Dignified or Ill Dignified?

a) The Querent is involved in a relationship with a needy and demanding man. She no longer loves him but feels she's unable to leave him.

_____

b) The Querent is listless and easily dominated. Her family takes advantage of her. The Querent doesn't feel she can stand up for herself and ask them to be more respectful.

_____

c) The Querent believes everything that everyone tells her and this has not served her well. She knows she needs to "grow up" and learn to tell when someone is being untruthful.

_____

d) The Querent admits that a few months ago she took some money at work because her financial situation was desperate. For a long time no one noticed but recently her boss has announced an audit. She's afraid she's going to be caught out.

_____

e) The Querent's father is a person who believes in speaking his mind. He recently told the Querent what he thinks of her husband and it has caused a great rift between them. The Querent wishes he would have kept his opinions to himself.

---

f) The Querent is an aggressive young man who enjoys bullying others. He likes to push people to see how far they will go.

---

g) The Querent is a student, diligent and hard working, but he has no social life. He is awkward and doesn't know what to say around people. He's more comfortable with books than with women and his social awkwardness keeps him from meeting new people.

---

h) The Querent was deeply in love with a woman and recently found out she was unfaithful to him. His friends had previously suspected something had been happening but the Querent refused to believe until one day he saw his partner with another man. He is profoundly hurt and disappointed.

KNIGHTS: COMBINATIONS

Look at these combinations and write down what they make you think of. There is no right or wrong answer, use your intuition. Remember that "ID" stands for Ill Dignified (Reversed)

Knight of Cups, Two of Coins

_____

_____

Knight of Cups, the Moon

_____

_____

Knight of Cups ID, Eight of Wands

_____

_____

Knight of Cups ID, the Chariot ID

_____

_____

Knight of Swords, Three of Wands ID

_____

_____

Knight of Swords, Four of Swords

_____

_____

Knight of Swords ID, the Star

_____

_____

Knight of Swords ID, the Hanged Man ID

_____

_____

Knight of Wands, Page of Cups ID,

_____

_____

Knight of Wands, Seven of Coins ID

_____

_____

Knight of Wands ID, Nine of Swords

_____

_____

Knight of Wands ID, Strength ID

_____

_____

Knight of Coins, the Emperor

_____

_____

Knight of Coins, Seven of Cups ID

_____

_____

Knight of Coins ID, Two of Coins

_____

_____

Knight of Coins ID, Wheel of Fortune ID

_____

_____

Which of these situations remind you of the various Queens? Are they Dignified or Ill Dignified?

a) The Querent's aunt is a lovely woman who loves being a hostess. She's welcoming and very kind.

_____

b) The Querent is verbally abusive with her husband and children. She is arrogant and considers other people to be beneath her. She is very domineering and she expects others to bend to her will.

_____

c) The Querent has known for sometime that her husband is unfaithful. She has not wanted to deal with it for fear of change, but the situation is not going away.

_____

d) The Querent's colleague is a vicious, mentally unstable woman who spreads rumours and invents dramatic situations in order to gain sympathy from others.

_____

e) The Querent's mother is a professor of law. She is incredibly good at her job and well respected in her field. She's not terribly maternal and she and the Querent often clash, but even the Querent admits that she is not a bad mother.

---

f) The Querent is a logical thinker and very good at discerning a person's character. She is loyal and true but she demands a lot of her friends.

---

g) The Querent's sister is convinced that she's psychic. She makes wild pronouncements that seem to have more to do with her dislike of certain people than of anything rooted in fact. Her accusations are tearing the family apart.

---

h) The Querent's mother-in-law is greedy and stingy with her money. She lives with the Querent and her husband and has accused them of trying to steal from her.

Look at these combinations and write down what they make you think of. There is no right or wrong answer, use your intuition. Remember that "ID" stands for Ill Dignified (Reversed)

Queen of Cups, Page of Coins

_____

_____

Queen of Cups, Eight of Wands

_____

_____

Queen of Cups ID, Two of Cups ID

_____

_____

Queen of Cups ID, High Priestess ID

_____

_____

Queen of Wands, Three of Coins ID

_____

_____

Queen of Wands, the Magician

_____

_____

Queen of Wands ID, the World ID

_____

_____

Queen of Wands ID, Justice

_____

_____

Queen of Coins, Four of Swords

_____

_____

Queen of Coins, Ten of Coins

_____

_____

Queen of Coins ID, Ten of Cups ID

_____

_____

Queen of Coins ID, the Lovers

_____

_____

Queen of Swords, Five of Swords

_____

_____

Queen of Swords, Three of Wands ID

_____

_____

Queen of Swords ID, Seven of Swords,

_____

_____

Queen of Swords ID, Three of Coins ID

_____

_____

Which of these situations remind you of the various Kings? Are they Dignified or Ill Dignified?

a) The Querent is involved with an older male. She loves him very much and has enjoyed their relationship but isn't sure he's terribly committed.

_____

b) The Querent is involved with a man who is verbally abusive toward her. He is a powerful person in the business world and has gained a reputation for being both unscrupulous and ruthless.

_____

c) The Querent is an energetic business man who is fair and decent. He's respected and works very hard in his field. He is dedicated and believes in justice and truth.

_____

d) The Querent knows that her father has been lying to her mother for some time now about his fidelity. She feels torn about the situation and afraid that if she tells the truth, she will be ostracized by one, if not both of her parents.

_____

e) The Querent's financial situation is out of control. He has no idea how much money comes in nor how much goes out. He spends entirely too much and will be facing ruin if he continues in this way.

---

f) The Querent's husband is a policeman of excellent reputation. Though he isn't particularly warm and emotional, he is absolutely correct in his behaviour.

---

g) The Querent's brother has ruined his marriage by engaging in a series of adulterous affairs. He believes himself to be misunderstood and can't understand why his family has taken his wife's side in this matter.

---

h) The Querent's grandfather is a kind man who lives simply but well. Although he doesn't look it, he's a millionaire several times over.

Look at these combinations and write down what they make you think of. There is no right or wrong answer, use your intuition. Remember that "ID" stands for Ill Dignified (Reversed)

King of Cups, Nine of Swords

_____

_____

King of Cups, Two of Swords

_____

_____

King of Cups ID, Eight of Cups

_____

_____

King of Cups ID, the Devil

_____

_____

King of Wands, Three of Coins

_____

_____

King of Wands, Eight of Wands

_____

_____

King of Wands ID, Four of Coins ID

_____

_____

King of Wands ID, the Magician ID

_____

_____

King of Coins, the Chariot

_____

_____

King of Coins, Six of Coins

_____

_____

King of Coins ID, Temperance ID

_____

_____

King of Coins ID, the Fool ID

_____

_____

King of Swords, Death

_____

_____

King of Swords, Two of Wands

_____

_____

King of Swords ID, Nine of Coins ID

_____

_____

King of Swords ID, High Priestess ID

_____

_____

MAJOR ARCANA EXERCISES

THE FOOL; THE MAGICIAN; THE HIGH PRIESTESS; THE EMPRESS; THE EMPEROR: SITUATIONS

Which of these situations remind you of the various Major Arcana cards? Are they Dignified or Ill Dignified?

a) The Querent is heading off to university. She is excited and nervous about the experience.

_____

b) The Querent's former lover is having his baby. Though they are not together anymore, the Querent is prepared to accept responsibility and be a father.

_____

c) The Querent is studying to be a doctor. She has been working for this for years and is very dedicated to her studies.

_____

d) The Querent and her husband are trying to have a baby and are having difficulty conceiving.

_____

e) The Querent gave a child up for adoption years ago and has now received a letter from the adoption agency to tell her son is looking for her.

She is afraid. Her family doesn't know about the existence of this other child.

_____

f) The Querent was a promising law student but simply quit after three years. He is stuck in a dead-end job and seems completely apathetic.

_____

g) The Querent has met a woman and they are deeply in love.

_____

h) The Querent wants to move to New York and become a famous model. She has never done any modelling but thinks she will be an instant star.

_____

i) The Querent's father is a difficult man for whom nothing is ever good enough. Attempts to win his approval are never successful.

_____

j) The Querent keeps having strange dreams which are telling her accurate things about friends and family members. She is finding the whole experience unsettling.

_____

THE FOOL; THE MAGICIAN; THE HIGH PRIESTESS; THE EMPRESS; THE EMPEROR: COMBINATIONS

Look at these combinations and write down what they make you think of. There is no right or wrong answer, use your intuition. Remember that "ID" stands for Ill Dignified (Reversed)

The Fool, Ace of Cups

_____

_____

The Fool, Three of Swords

_____

_____

The Fool ID, the Hermit

_____

_____

The Fool ID, Five of Coins

_____

_____

The Magician, Seven of Coins

_____

_____

The Magician, Page of Swords ID

_____

_____

The Magician ID, the Hanged Man

_____

_____

The Magician ID, Two of Wands ID

_____

_____

The High Priestess, Four of Wands ID

_____

_____

The High Priestess, Six of Cups

_____

_____

The High Priestess ID, the Tower

_____

_____

The High Priestess ID, the Chariot

_____

_____

The Empress, Ace of Cups

_____

_____

The Empress, Four of Cups

_____

_____

The Empress ID, Queen of Swords

_____

_____

The Empress ID, Nine of Swords

_____

_____

The Emperor, Four of Cups ID

_____

_____

The Emperor, Three of Wands

_____

_____

The Emperor ID, Ten of Coins ID

_____

_____

The Emperor ID, Justice

_____

_____

Which of these situations remind you of the various Major Arcana cards? Are they Dignified or Ill Dignified?

a) The Querent is involved in a relationship with a married woman.

_____

b) The Querent's plans to move ahead with her career are stalled and she's frustrated.

_____

c) The Querent has just lost her husband to a long illness and is feeling depleted, tired and sad.

_____

d) The Querent is starting a new relationship with a woman to whom he's very attracted.

_____

e) The Querent's father is rigid and dogmatic. His views are narrow and he imposes them on others.

_____

f) The Querent loves going to parties and clubs, she rarely spends any time alone. Lately she's starting to feel dissatisfied with her lifestyle and wonders if there's something deeper.

_____

g) The Querent is moving to a new town to start a new job.

_____

h) The Querent has just lost her job and is feeling depressed. She's not sure how to manage over the next few months.

_____

i) The Querent is lonely and feels that he has no friends. He has been alone so long he doesn't really even know how to meet people.

_____

j) The Querent's uncle is a learned man who has offered excellent guidance and advice.

_____

Look at these combinations and write down what they make you think of. There is no right or wrong answer, use your intuition. Remember that "ID" stands for Ill Dignified (Reversed)

The Hierophant, Three of Swords

_____

_____

The Hierophant, Six of Coins ID

_____

_____

The Hierophant ID, King of Coins ID

_____

_____

The Hierophant ID, Two of Swords

_____

_____

The Lovers, Six of Cups

_____

_____

The Lovers, Ace of Cups ID

_____

_____

The Lovers ID, Ten of Cups ID

_____

_____

The Lovers ID, the Star ID

_____

_____

The Chariot, Three of Coins

_____

_____

The Chariot, Five of Swords

_____

_____

The Chariot ID, Eight of Cups ID

_____

_____

The Chariot ID, the High Priestess

_____

_____

Strength, Justice

_____

_____

Strength, the Emperor

_____

_____

Strength ID, Queen of Swords ID

_____

_____

Strength ID, Ten of Wands

_____

_____

The Hermit, Two of Coins ID

_____

_____

The Hermit, Four of Wands ID

_____

_____

The Hermit ID, Four of Cups ID

_____

_____

The Hermit ID, the Moon ID

_____

_____

THE WHEEL OF FORTUNE; JUSTICE; THE HANGED MAN; DEATH; TEMPERANCE; THE DEVIL: SITUATIONS

Which of these situations remind you of the various Major Arcana cards? Are they Dignified or Ill Dignified?

a) The Querent finds his life spiralling out of control. Where once he had an easy life, he's having problems at work, home and financially.

_____

b) The Querent is entering a period where things are much better than they had been previously.

_____

c) The Querent was successful in a law suit against a former business partner who cheated her.

_____

d) The Querent's boss is punishing her for things she did not do, and blaming her for mistakes made by her colleagues.

_____

e) The Querent lives a busy life but is finding more and more that he needs to think about which direction his life is taking.

_____

f)   The Querent lives at a frenetic pace and refuses to slow down. Her life and her relationships are deliberately kept at a superficial level.

---

g)   The Querent's marriage is breaking down.

---

h)   The Querent has a difficult relationship with her best friend. It's been hard for months now, but things seem a bit better at the moment. In truth, the Querent does not imagine their friendship will survive for much longer.

---

i)   The Querent has been spending a lot of money lately. She finds when she buys something she gets a rush and feels happy for a while. She's worried it might get out of control.

---

j)   The Querent recently found that her husband had hid bottles of alcohol around the house. She's worried about him as she thought he'd quit drinking months ago.

---

k) The Querent is in a relationship which is unhealthy and unloving, but she feels she can't leave.

---

l) The Querent's partner is becoming more and more negative. Being with him isn't fun or exciting any more. His negativity is driving people away and he doesn't seem to realise his part in this.

THE WHEEL OF FORTUNE; JUSTICE; THE HANGED MAN; DEATH; TEMPERANCE; THE DEVIL: COMBINATIONS

Look at these combinations and write down what they make you think of. There is no right or wrong answer, use your intuition. Remember that "ID" stands for Ill Dignified (Reversed)

Wheel of Fortune, Two of Coins ID

_____

_____

Wheel of Fortune, the High Priestess

_____

_____

Wheel of Fortune ID, the Magician ID

_____

_____

Wheel of Fortune ID, Six of Swords

_____

_____

Justice, Nine of Swords

_____

_____

Justice, Ace of Swords

_____

_____

Justice ID, Death

_____

_____

Justice ID, Empress ID

_____

_____

The Hanged Man, Two of Swords,

_____

_____

The Hanged Man, the Devil

_____

_____

The Hanged Man ID, Nine of Wands

_____

_____

The Hanged Man ID, Five of Coins

_____

_____

Death, Nine of Coins ID

Death, the Chariot

Death ID, the Tower ID

Death ID, Page of Cups ID

137

Temperance, Ace of Wands

_____

_____

Temperance, Five of Wands ID

_____

_____

Temperance ID, Seven of Coins

_____

_____

Temperance ID, Six of Swords ID

_____

_____

The Devil, Six of Cups

_____

_____

The Devil, Four of Coins

_____

_____

The Devil ID, Knight of Swords ID

_____

_____

The Devil ID, the Magician ID

_____

_____

Which of these situations remind you of the various Major Arcana cards? Are they Dignified or Ill Dignified?

a) The Querent will lose his job unless he makes his quota next month. He can do it, but it's going to be a lot of work.

_____

b) The Querent is unrealistic in his dreams of a love affair with a woman who clearly does not care for him.

_____

c) The Querent is involved in a business deal with people she does not entirely trust. She feels they are lying to her somehow.

_____

d) The Querent has been visiting a therapist and is feeling better than she ever has before.

_____

e) The Querent has been going through a tough time but he recognises that the end of his troubles is at hand and that things will get better soon.

_____

f) The Querent has been accused of stealing money from work. It wasn't her, and she doesn't know who the guilty party is.

_____

g) The Querent has finished university and now has several good job offers. He is excited to begin this new stage of his life.

_____

h) The Querent has reached her weight and fitness goal only to find it's not as exciting as she'd hoped it would be. Her life is basically exactly the same, only her clothes are smaller.

_____

i) The Querent's life has completely fallen apart.

_____

j) The Querent was cheating on her husband and has been caught.

_____

k) The Querent has just found out that her parents lied to her for many years and that she was adopted. She's feeling very isolated and hurt.

_____

I) The Querent is hoping for a reunion with a lost love.

THE TOWER; THE STAR; THE MOON; THE SUN; JUDGEMENT; THE WORLD: COMBINATIONS

Look at these combinations and write down what they make you think of. There is no right or wrong answer, use your intuition. Remember that "ID" stands for Ill Dignified (Reversed)

The Tower, Ten of Swords

_____

_____

The Tower, Two of Swords

_____

_____

The Tower ID, the World

_____

_____

The Tower ID, the High Priestess

_____

_____

The Star, Eight of Wands

_____

_____

The Star, Page of Cups

_____

_____

The Star ID, Three of Wands ID

_____

_____

The Star ID, Six of Coins

_____

_____

The Moon, Magician ID

_____

_____

The Moon, Six of Wands ID

_____

_____

The Moon ID, Knight of Swords

_____

_____

The Moon ID, Ace of Cups ID

_____

_____

The Sun, the Empress

_____

_____

The Sun, Nine of Swords ID

_____

_____

The Sun ID, Six of Swords

_____

_____

The Sun ID, Six of Wands ID

_____

_____

Judgement, Ace of Swords ID

_____

_____

Judgement, Two of Wands ID

_____

_____

Judgement ID, the Hanged Man ID

_____

_____

Judgement ID, Three of Cups ID

_____

_____

The World, Ace of Coins

The World, Nine of Cups

The World ID, Seven of Cups ID

The World ID, Page of Wands

READING COMBINATIONS

The following is an exercise in reading combinations of cards. Look at the following combinations and decide how you would read them. Decide whether they can be read as cause and effect or if they modify / intensify one another. Keep in mind that for every card there are multiple meanings and that the same combination of cards could mean different things for different Querents, so flexibility is important. There is no right or wrong answer. Use your intuition. Remember that ID stands for Ill Dignified.

Example:
Three of Swords, Two of Coins

After an especially difficult time emotionally, the Querent needs to try to enjoy herself more. Go out, socialise, see people and try to have some fun. It may not be easy, but it is necessary to spend some time with friends who lift her spirits and she will see that life goes on.

Ten of Swords, Ace of Wands ID

_____

_____

Eight of Cups, Knight of Swords

_____

_____

Page of Wands, Empress

_____

_____

The Lovers ID, Ace of Swords ID

_____

_____

Judgement ID, the Fool ID

_____

Knight of Coins ID, the Star ID

_____

_____

Five of Swords ID, Page of Cups

_____

_____

King of Coins, Three of Cups

_____

_____

Nine of Wands, Five of Wands ID

_____

_____

Six of Swords, Eight of Coins

_____

_____

Four of Swords, Four of Coins

_____

_____

The Hermit ID, the Sun

_____

Two of Cups, King of Swords

Death, Knight of Wands ID

Queen of Cups ID, the Hanged Man ID

Seven of Coins, Three of Coins

_____

_____

Four of Wands, Six of Wands ID

_____

_____

Two of Wands, Page of Coins ID

_____

_____

Seven of Cups ID, Three of Wands

Ten of Wands ID, the World ID

Temperance, Eight of Wands

Nine of Swords ID, Six of Cups ID

Seven of Wands, Two of Coins

_____

_____

Justice, Three of Swords

_____

_____

Ace of Cups ID, Nine of Cups ID

_____

_____

The Tower, Queen of Swords ID

Four of Cups, the Chariot

King of Wands, Six of Coins

Strength ID, Queen of Wands ID

157

Emperor ID, High Priestess

_____

_____

Two of Swords, Ace of Coins

_____

_____

Page of Swords, Seven of Swords ID

_____

_____

Five of Cups, Devil ID

_____

Nine of Coins ID, Knight of Cups ID

Nine of Swords ID, Queen of Cups

Hierophant, King of Cups ID

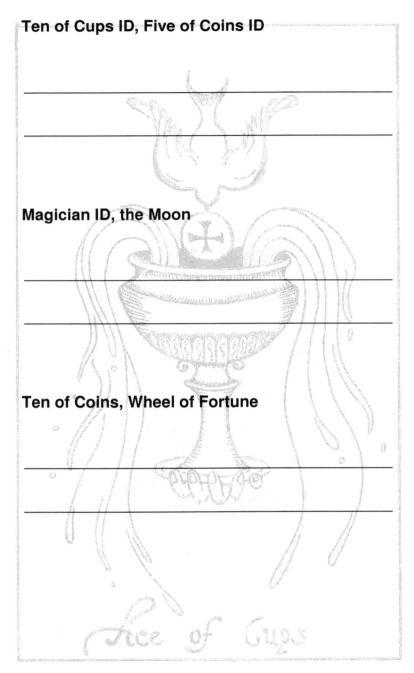

Ten of Cups ID, Five of Coins ID

_____

_____

Magician ID, the Moon

_____

_____

Ten of Coins, Wheel of Fortune

_____

_____

SCENARIOS

The following scenarios are an exercise in reading backwards. Where the previous exercises required that you look at specific cards and extract meaning from them, this exercise is more fluid. Here you have a scenario, which you simply read and then decide which cards in the tarot deck you would connect to it. Will these cards be Dignified or Ill Dignified? Will there be a combination of cards? You decide.

Take a look at the following scenarios and decide which cards would best describe them.

Elena is very much involved with a man much older than her. He has a great deal of influence on her, choosing her clothing, her course of study, films to see etc. and now he's beginning to criticise her friends and tell her that they are stupid, unworthy of her and that she shouldn't spend so much time with them. At the same time, Elena has noticed that he is drinking more heavily.

_____

_____

Steven is engaged to be married to a girl he's been dating since high school but there's a lack of enthusiasm on his part. The engagement has been extended several times as he continues to insist that the time isn't right. The truth is that he is unsure of his decision to marry this girl and feels that he asked her to marry him simply because they had been together for so long and that it was expected of him. His fiancée is unhappy and they fight a lot but neither of them is willing to break off their relationship.

_____

_____

Margaret is cheating on her husband of ten years with a co-worker. She is afraid that her husband suspects something but she feels unable to either stop the relationship or tell her husband the truth. She describes the affair with her colleague as "magical" and even though she admits that her lover has a lot of faults, she is convinced he is better for her than her husband.

_____

_____

A couple has trying to become pregnant for years with no success. The strain is taking a toll on their relationship and they are beginning to argue more. The woman feels that the quest for a baby is beginning to consume her life and her husband wishes they could just stop. Both of them are thinking back to the beginning of their relationship when times were better. There are feelings of bitterness and disappointment.

_____

_____

A middle aged man is stealing from his company. It started small, exaggerating on expense accounts, charging lunches for clients who had in fact been friends, but it's escalated as his personal financial problems have deepened. He lives in constant fear of being discovered and is beginning to crack under the strain. Also, he feels guilty because his boss is a man he likes and respects. He cannot understand how he ended up in this place and he feels disgusted and disappointed with himself.

_____

_____

Sophie has just found out that a friend she confided in has betrayed her by spreading untrue gossip about her. He has also told a lot of people things which she has specifically asked him to keep secret. She cannot understand what would motivate someone who she took to be a friend to be so careless. Now she feels she's being ostracised and judged by people who now know her most personal secrets.

_____

_____

Peter has been helping his brother Mark for years with his problems of addiction. Mark is able to get his addiction under control for some time and inevitably falls off the wagon again and again. Peter has given his brother money, a place to stay, support. Sums of money have recently started to go missing from his wallet. Peter is disappointed, sad and angry but also feels that he is responsible for his brother.

Adeline complains that her husband has been working too hard and that his frequent absences from home are beginning to affect their marriage. He is no longer affectionate and seems to be under a great deal of strain, losing his temper easily or being remote and cold.

Allan has spent his whole life trying to please his father. His father is a cold man, unreasonable and demanding. Nothing Allan has ever done is good enough. His father constantly compares Allan to his other brothers and sisters and makes unkind remarks about Allan's wife and children. Despite this, Allan still yearns for approval and warmth from his father.

Marie has been experiencing money problems. Her spending is out of control and when she is under stress she goes shopping. Lately, the purchases have been getting larger and larger and the bills more daunting. She has stopped opening her mail because she thinks that if she doesn't know about it, she won't have to deal with it. Creditors are starting to knock on the door and she's in danger of losing her home.

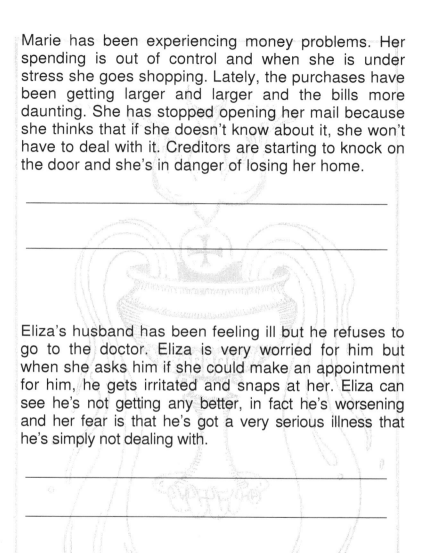

Eliza's husband has been feeling ill but he refuses to go to the doctor. Eliza is very worried for him but when she asks him if she could make an appointment for him, he gets irritated and snaps at her. Eliza can see he's not getting any better, in fact he's worsening and her fear is that he's got a very serious illness that he's simply not dealing with.

Faye's mother is very demanding. She's always been difficult and hard to please, but lately she's become aggressive. She's convinced that people are stealing from her and her paranoia is getting out of hand. Faye is worried about her mother and it's affecting all facets of her life. She feels she's neglecting her husband and children as she's constantly at her mother's house trying to sort things out for her. Faye is tired and feels overwhelmed and sad.

_____

_____

A troubled film star everyone said was washed up and ruined came back after years out of the public eye. She starred in a film which was a critical and popular success and found herself at the top of her game, sought out by producers and directors. Suddenly, she's faced with the same temptations which got her into trouble in the first place.

_____

_____

Sam, 18, is going away to university. He's full of hope and excited about the prospect of being on his own. He's determined to do well in school and make something of himself. Sam is a dreamy young man, a bit naive, but with a good heart.

_____

_____

Quentin has studied very hard for years to become a lawyer. He has diligently and carefully applied himself to his studies and now he has his degree and a job in a law firm. All of this is nice, but he feels a bit empty and lonely inside. Now that he has achieved his goals, he wonders what else there is for him.

_____

_____

Susan has been spreading rumours about a woman she doesn't like at work. The trouble is that this woman is up for a promotion and could very likely end up being Susan's boss. If word of the nasty comments Susan made get back to the woman, she could be out of a job. Susan isn't sure her colleagues will keep quiet as she doesn't get along very well with a few of them and she suspects they would be happy to see her in trouble. She does not recognise that her bellicose nature has anything to do with the trouble she's currently in.

_____

_____

Gavin is forty-five years old. He's bored with his job and finds it unfulfilling. He dreams of going back to university but he's afraid that after so many years of not being in school, it will be an impossible task. He's worried about looking ridiculous in a class full of young people. Instead he goes to work each day and does a job he dislikes. His unhappiness is creating discord in his family life. He and his wife barely speak about anything other than their children. Gavin is impatient and snaps frequently. Even his boss has noticed that he is not an enthusiastic employee.

_____

_____

Kendra's neighbours are difficult people. They throw parties at all hours, stay up late and make a lot of noise. They have three dogs which bark and howl and frighten Kendra's children. They don't mow their lawn or take care of their garden and trash is piling up. Kendra has been thinking about selling her house but she realises that with neighbours like these, it will be next to impossible.

_____

_____

Harry is fifty-six years old. He was recently fired from his job after a conflict with his boss. At first he was hopeful that he would find work quickly, but he's finding it far more difficult than he imagined. He's discouraged and is starting to stay home more and avoid the company of old friends. He feels ashamed and embarrassed at his reduced circumstances.

Diane is becoming more and more involved with a fringe religious group. Her involvement with them began after her husband died three years previously. She spends very little time now with family and friends and more and more time with the church and its charismatic preacher. She is donating large amounts of money to the church. Her family is worried about her but she is increasingly seeing them as sinners and as people best avoided. Where she used to be sunny and open minded, she's become rigidly dogmatic.

Serena has a great desire to learn to be a chef. She reads cookbooks, watches cooking shows on television and dreams of one day having her own restaurant. She has recently taken a part time job in a restaurant kitchen so she can learn about how a kitchen runs. On top of her full-time job, it's a great deal of work, but Serena is very happy. She loves the idea of creating a space where people can come together and eat and socialise and she is determined to reach this goal.

_____

_____

Daniel is struggling with Multiple Sclerosis. He used to be athletic, healthy and active and now he has difficulty with simple motor-skills. He finds more and more that he is depressed and unhappy. Because he can no longer participate in sports, he finds his social life is suddenly quite empty. He is lonely and afraid but he is also too proud to admit that he's feeling this way.

_____

_____

Kit is longing for a relationship long past. She was with a man for seven years until he left for another relationship. Though it appears that Kit has moved on, a new job, a new partner, a new city, the reality is that she still dreams of this lost love. She wonders what he is doing, if he is happy, if he thinks of her. She dreams about what would happen if they were to accidentally meet on the street one day. Her desire for the past is interfering with her ability to enjoy the present.

_____

Jack has been avoiding the responsibilities of adulthood. He lives in his mother's basement. He is sporadically employed in menial jobs. If he does meet a woman and enters into a relationship, his chronic immaturity destroys the romance within a short time. Jack's mother blames a series of "stupid girls" on her son's unhappiness and makes excuses for his failure to grow up and participate in life. For his part, Jack is growing increasingly dissatisfied with his life and ashamed of his circumstances.

_____

_____

Jerry lost his house due to his gambling habit. He used to work as a salesman but he lost that job as his addiction took over his life. His family can't seem to get through to him. His wife loves him but doesn't know how to help him.

_____

_____

Zara has taken on a new project which is proving to be heavier than she had originally imagined. Her partners in this venture are not as helpful as she thought they would be and increasingly she is finding the burden rests on her shoulders. She is tired all the time as her sleep is affected by stress and worry.

_____

_____

Annie is 80 years old and has amassed a sizeable amount of money due to wise investments. She talks about money incessantly and what she wants done with it after she dies. She believes her relatives are nice to her only because they want her money. She holds her wealth over their heads and threatens to cut them off.

_____

_____

Norma is angry and mean spirited. She believes that her way of life is the only way, and that anything that deviates from her narrow perspective is wrong and stupid. She's critical, hurtful and freely gives her opinion where none is asked for. Her family and friends are starting to avoid her.

_____

_____

Sally got up the courage to approach a man she's known for years and tell him of her romantic feelings for him. She was hoping he would feel the same way. Instead, he's told her he needs to think about the situation. He's been thinking for some time now, but Sally refuses to give up hope. Her friends think she's being unrealistic.

_____

_____

Julia works in a clothing store. She occasionally let her friends in after-hours and they would try items on and if they liked something, she would give it to them without asking them to pay. Julia thinks her boss suspects something.

_____

_____

Lana has been studying yoga for fifteen years. She has recently started teaching. She finds it amazingly rewarding and it has brought peace and prosperity into her life.

_____

_____

Hector has a difficult time managing his weight. His appetite is enormous and he often eats in response to stress or boredom. He's beginning to have difficulty moving but he doesn't seem to be able to stop himself.

_____

_____

Penny is a forty-seven year old wife and mother and a compulsive shoplifter. She literally can't stop herself. She's been caught five times now. Her family is ashamed and embarrassed and her husband has warned her that he will not bail her out if she's arrested again.

_____

_____

Mark is in an abusive relationship. His wife is physically aggressive with him. He doesn't know what to do.

_____

_____

Darlene is a busy mother of three. She's organised, dynamic and enthusiastic. She's recently written a book about parenting and is looking for a publisher.

_____

_____

Yvonne has been seeing a psychic. This woman charges a lot of money but never seems to tell

Yvonne anything. Some of the things she says about Yvonne's family or departed relatives are simply wrong. Yvonne still wants to believe this woman and continues to go and see her.

Kay's son disappeared twenty years ago, vanishing without a trace. She has never been the same since and has suffered year after year, waiting to hear news of him. She believes he ran away from home because he was angry with his parents. She feels incredibly guilty for not having been the perfect mother.

Oliver recently found out his wife has been drinking on the sly. He was surprised but he also feels guilty because he wonders how it is they've grown so far apart that he hadn't noticed earlier.

Helena suspects her daughter is a compulsive liar. She's overheard her fifteen year old daughter speaking on the phone and telling her friends things which were completely untrue. Helena values truth and has no idea where her daughter would have learned such behaviour.

_____

_____

Ursula has a crush on her married neighbour. At first she simply thought he was a nice, attractive man. It has grown into something like an obsession. She thinks about him constantly and tries to finds excuses to be out in her garden when he's outside. The man's wife seems to notice but Ursula doesn't care.

_____

_____

Tina has found drug paraphernalia in her seventeen year old son's school bag. She's disappointed, worried and angry.

_____

_____

Olivia has been married for three years now and her marriage is comfortable, if not exciting. Olivia ran into an ex-boyfriend on the street one day. Since then, she's been dreaming about him and wondering if they could meet up again. She has forgotten any negative qualities her old lover had and now finds herself comparing him favourably to her husband.

_____

_____

Barbara is fifty-seven years old and very lonely. She has a difficult time socialising and making friends and finds that she would like to be around people but increasingly she does not know how. Her sense of isolation is causing her sadness.

_____

_____

Jane is a forty-eight year old woman whose mother is dying. Jane has always been close to her mother and is having a difficult time watching her become increasingly weaker and frailer.

_____

_____

Frank has recently retired from a high stress job and finds he has no idea what to do with himself. He's bored and lonely and finds he has nothing to fill his days.

_____

_____

Trevor made a terrible mistake and drove home after having a few drinks. He caused an accident which hurt another person badly and he is facing criminal charges. Trevor feels sick about what he's done and is consumed by guilt and self-loathing.

_____

_____

Sam and Jenny are getting a divorce after fifteen years of marriage and three children. Division of property and money is proving to be a source of acrimony and they are bitterly arguing in front of their children.

_____

_____

Hilary and Tyler are getting a divorce after five years of marriage. They are determined to keep things as amicable as possible and are even seeing a counsellor in order to make the break as compassionate and decent as possible.

_____

_____

Kandace has been offered a job in India. She is exited about the prospect of living in a new country but is also quite nervous about the huge change that emigrating would entail.

_____

_____

Dolly has recently discovered that the contractor who did some home repairs for her did a shoddy job and now she is left with more damage than she originally had. She is angry and considering legal action.

_____

_____

Emily is nineteen, pregnant and in denial. She is wearing large, loose clothes in hopes of disguising her condition. She refuses to think about her pregnancy and hopes no one will notice. Her parents think she is getting fat. It's only a matter of time before they understand the truth.

_____

_____

Leila is exhausted. She's been working three jobs and looking after her aging parents. She feels as though her nerves are stretched to the breaking point and she desperately needs a break. She's having problems sleeping and has lost her sense of joy.

_____

_____

James is having a conflict with his roommates regarding money. James lost his job recently and is having a difficult time coming up with money for rent and bills. His roommates are not being very understanding about it and he feels put upon and hurt.

_____

_____

Ivan is thinking about adopting a vegetarian lifestyle for reasons of health and ethics. His family is unimpressed with his choice and Ivan is finding that he needs to defend his new-found ideas to the people he's closest to.

Rose has been diagnosed with breast cancer. She is extremely worried not just about herself, but about her young family. She is scheduled to begin treatments very soon.

Estella's son is experiencing great problems in school. He's failing almost all his subjects and displays no outward concern about it. Estella has had many meetings with his teachers and though she continuously stresses to her son the importance of education, she does not seem to be getting through to him.

Melissa threw a party for her husband's birthday and during the celebration, someone went into their bedroom and stole money and jewellery from their dresser. Melissa is aghast that a friend of hers would do such a thing. She has no idea who it could have been and is worried about making any sort of accusation.

_____

_____

Jade's younger sister was diagnosed with schizophrenia years ago. It has always fallen to Jade to help care for her sister, and lately her behaviour has become increasingly difficult. Jade suspects her sister is off her medication and is in need of help.

_____

_____

John and Kathy have been together for nine years and their relationship has been getting stale and the joy has gone out of it. They have both decided to work on their marriage and are both attempting to make their lives more interesting and happier again.

_____

_____

William has received an inheritance from an uncle he barely knew. He was surprised and also grateful as the money has come at the perfect moment.

_____

_____

Zoë has been fighting with her family for years and it came to a head recently over the holidays. She has never seen eye to eye with her parents and she has become more and more disillusioned with the way they live their lives and the expectations they have of their children. Zoë is considering breaking off from them entirely.

_____

_____

Carrie doesn't like her step-mother and never has. They have never been close and Carrie feels as though her relationship with her father has suffered immeasurably due to her step-mother's constant interference.

_____

_____

Aurora went to a dinner party at a friend's house and got food poisoning. She ended up in the hospital for three days and was very, very sick, as were the other guests at the party. This has created a sense of awkwardness between Aurora and her friend.

_____

_____

Donna's son goes to school with her boss's daughter. Recently she discovered that the daughter has been bullying her son and telling him that he can't do anything about it because if he does, his mother will be fired from her job.

_____

_____

Gina's boyfriend of six years left her recently. Gina is understandably sad about it but has decided to take this opportunity to make some changes in her life. She's taken up some new hobbies, is taking a history class at the university and has had a make-over, changing her appearance and wardrobe.

_____

_____

Ira has been planning a long journey to Tibet, India and China. The trip should last about six months and Ira has taken a leave of absence from his job. He's looking forward to this adventure and is busy reading as much as he can about the places he wants to visit. He's also taking some language lessons.

_____

_____

Sybil is chronically late for everything – work, appointments, meetings with friends etc. She is in danger of losing her job if she isn't able to get herself organised properly. She does not understand why she is unable to keep appointments in a timely fashion or go to work on time.

_____

_____

SITUATION EXERCISE ANSWERS

The following are answers to the "situations" section of each group of cards. They correspond to meanings given in The Open Minded Tarot: A Practical Guide, and may or may not correspond to the meanings that you connect to cards. Feel free to attach your own meanings to each of the examples given. Tarot is about your path, not my ideas.

Aces
a) Ace of Wands
b) Ace of Cups ID
c) Ace of Coins
d) Ace of Swords
e) Ace of Swords ID
f) Ace of Wands ID
g) Ace of Coins ID
h) Ace of Cups

Twos
a) Two of Swords
b) Two of Cups
c) Two of Coins
d) Two of Wands ID
e) Two of Wands
f) Two of Coins ID
g) Two of Cups ID
h) Two of Swords ID

Threes
a) Three of Coins
b) Three of Cups
c) Three of Cups ID
d) Three of Swords
e) Three of Wands
f) Three of Wands ID
g) Three of Swords ID
h) Three of Coins ID

Fours
a) Four of Wands
b) Four of Swords ID
c) Four of Coins ID
d) Four of Cups
e) Four of Cups ID
f) Four of Swords
g) Four of Wands ID
h) Four of Coins

Fives
a) Five of Swords ID
b) Five of Wands
c) Five of Cups ID
d) Five of Swords
e) Five of Coins
f) Five of Coins ID
g) Five of Cups
h) Five of Wands ID

Sixes
a) Six of Cups ID
b) Six of Wands ID
c) Six of Coins
d) Six of Coins ID
e) Six of Swords
f) Six of Wands
g) Six of Cups
h) Six of Swords ID

Sevens
a) Seven of Coins
b) Seven of Cups
c) Seven of Wands
d) Seven of Swords
e) Seven of Coins ID
f) Seven of Swords ID
g) Seven of Wands ID
h) Seven of Cups ID

Eights
a) Eight of Wands
b) Eight of Wands ID
c) Eight of Coins
d) Eight of Cups ID
e) Eight of Swords
f) Eight of Cups
g) Eight of Coins ID
h) Eight of Swords ID

Nines
a) Nine of Cups
b) Nine of Cups ID
c) Nine of Swords
d) Nine of Wands
e) Nine of Coins
f) Nine of Swords ID
g) Nine of Coins ID
h) Nine of Wands ID

Tens
a) Ten of Cups
b) Ten of Cups ID
c) Ten of Swords ID
d) Ten of Coins
e) Ten of Coins ID
f) Ten of Wands ID
g) Ten of Wands
h) Ten of Swords

Pages
a) Page of Cups ID
b) Page of Coins ID
c) Page of Swords ID
d) Page of Cups
e) Page of Wands ID
f) Page of Coins
g) Page of Wands
h) Page of Swords

Knights
a) Knight of Cups ID
b) Knight of Wands ID
c) Knight of Wands
d) Knight of Coins ID
e) Knight of Swords
f) Knight of Swords ID
g) Knight of Coins
h) Knight of Cups

Queens
a) Queen of Coins
b) Queen of Wands ID
c) Queen of Cups ID
d) Queen of Swords ID
e) Queen of Wands
f) Queen of Swords
g) Queen of Cups ID
h) Queen of Coins ID

Kings
a) King of Cups
b) King of Wands ID
c) King of Wands
d) King of Swords ID
e) King of Coins ID
f) King of Swords
g) King of Cups ID
h) King of Coins

The Fool, The Magician, The High Priestess, The Empress, The Emperor
a) The Fool
b) The Emperor
c) The Magician
d) The Empress ID
e) The High Priestess ID
f) The Magician ID
g) The Empress
h) The Fool ID
i) The Emperor ID
j) The High Priestess

The Hierophant, The Lovers, The Chariot, Strength, The Hermit

a) The Lovers ID
b) The Chariot ID
c) Strength
d) The Lovers
e) The Hierophant ID

f) The Hermit
g) The Hermit
h) The Chariot
i) Strength ID
j) The Hermit ID
k) The Hierophant

The Wheel of Fortune, Justice, The Hanged Man, Death, Temperance, The Devil

a) The Wheel of Fortune ID
b) The Wheel of Fortune
c) Justice
d) Justice ID
e) The Hanged Man
f) The Hanged Man ID

g) Death
h) Death ID
i) Temperance
j) Temperance ID
k) The Devil
l) The Devil ID

The Tower, The Star, The Moon, The Sun, Judgement, The World

a) The Word ID
b) The Star ID
c) The Moon
d) The World
e) The Tower ID
f) Judgement ID

g) The Sun
h) The Sun ID
i) The Tower
j) Judgement
k) The Moon ID
l) The Star

ACKNOWLEDGEMENTS

I wish to thank the following people for their help, patience and generosity while writing The Open Minded Tarot Workbook and The Open Minded Tarot: A Practical Guide:

To Martin, thanks so much for your encouragement. Your kind words mean more than you know. To Gail, without your hard work and excellent ideas, this would never have seen the light of day. To Chloe Johnson, for originally inspiring this book. To my friends and family for just being who they are. I would also like to thank Luna Apollonio, the talented young artist who illustrated the front cover. Anyone interested in contacting Luna can do so at:
lunaapollonioart@gmail.com.

I would like to wish everyone reading this good luck and an enjoyable and enriching journey into the world of tarot. Learning to read tarot is as much about human nature as it is about actual cards. Know the cards, know yourself.

Best wishes.

Kate Ross